The Cowboy

The Cowboy

Vincent Paul Rennert

CROWELL-COLLIER PRESS, *New York*

COLLIER-MACMILLAN LTD., *London*

for Paul, Cathy, and Peter

Contents

❁

The Cowboy

1 · Origins

✽

THE AMERICAN COWBOY of the movies, television, and most novels and adventure stories is a man of many colorful talents. He has been shown or described as a man who either swept the Old West clean of outlaws, or became one himself. With his two six-guns blazing, his custom-tailored shirt showing every muscle, and his clean-shaven face bright in the sun, he roared through frontier towns scaring the local citizens clear out of their wits. He fought battles against hostile Indians, or overturned gambling house tables to give the villain his due. At least, so we have been told.

This description of the old-time cowboy is completely false on most counts and highly exaggerated on all the rest. Worst of all, it does not contain a hint of what the real cowboy did or why most boys dreamed of some day being cowboys too.

The cowboy's job was to round up, brand, and drive

cattle. He was a man, often hardly out of his teens, who loved the freedom the work on the range gave him. He was uneasy in polite society and felt at home and relaxed only when alone or with other cowboys. This did not mean that he shirked responsibility, for his job carried with it duties and obligations that would have humbled many another man. Far out on the trail, in company with only eight or ten other cowboys, he watched over cattle worth many thousands of dollars and delivered them despite great hardships.

The cowboy came into his own in Texas just after the Civil War, hit his peak of activity in the early 1880s, and was already passing into history by the early 1890s.

The time involved was only about twenty-five years, but during that time some 40,000 young men drove 10,000,000 head of cattle and at least 1,000,000 horses over the trails leading east, west, but mostly north, out of Texas.

The young cowboy was a paid horseman. The pay scale ranged from a low of ten dollars a month for a beginner during the earliest days on the range up to sixty dollars for an experienced puncher at the height of the big trail drives.

But whatever the cowboy's salary, it was little measured against the job to be done. The cowboy played

The cowboy was at home on the open range among his fellow cowboys
and the cattle he watched over, rounded up, branded, and drove to market

a very important part in the opening up of the frontier. He worked with once-domesticated cattle that had been turned loose on the land to multiply. These half wild animals were unpredictable and might turn mean and tricky to handle at the most unlikely times. And the cowboy had to drive these cattle over vast distances through a part of the country that was not only unsettled but also largely unexplored except by the Indian tribes.

Beyond this, the cowboy had to brave the extremes of weather common in the range country. In the summer in the Southwest the heat sometimes reached 115 degrees or higher in the shade, and in the winter on the Northwest plains many a cow or horse froze to death in the wild and often sudden blizzards.

This cowboy, or puncher, as he was sometimes called, did not spring up like a weed after a spring rain: he was a long time in coming. He acquired his skills and his toughness through the slow process of experience, and his reason for being goes back several hundred years, to the introduction of the first livestock to North America.

When Christopher Columbus landed in the New World for the second time, in 1493, he brought with him a number of cattle and horses. One book notes that Columbus arrived on the island of Santo Domingo with "fifteen hundred men . . . with provisions for their subsistence, with the seeds of all the plants that were thought likely to thrive in this hot and damp climate, and with the domestic animals of the old hemisphere, of which there was not one in the new."

Then, in 1519, Hernando Cortes left Cuba and sailed for Mexico with sixteen horses, plus soldiers, guns, and crossbows. Just two years later Gregorio de Villalobos arrived from Santo Domingo, bringing with him seven calves. This was the beginning of what would prove to be, some 350 years later, the greatest herds of cattle and bands of horses the world had ever known.

Even before their arrival in the New World, the Spaniards had listened to tales of the Seven Cities of Cibola, which were, like the Fountain of Youth, supposed to exist. It was said that the streets were paved with gold and that quantities of jewels were there for the taking. The dreams of Cibola grew more vivid when the Spaniards reached Mexico, and they were anxious to find the fabled land, though its exact location was not, of course, known. And so, on March 7, 1539, under the command of Marcos de Niza, a Franciscan, an expedition crossed into what is now Arizona, and its members became the first "outsiders" in this part of future United States territory. The Zuni Indians, already in command of the area, were not very hospitable toward their visitors and allowed only a handful to escape alive.

The lure of fabulous treasures made a return visit certain, and on the second attempt the Spaniards sent along a well-equipped army under the command of Francisco Vásquez de Coronado. Included were 1,300 horses. The year was 1540, and Coronado's group, though it suffered substantial losses, overpowered the Zuni and set up a base. The victory was a hollow one, and in 1542 the army returned to Mexico, without gold or jewels. Left behind were the Spaniards' abandoned cattle and horses, which managed to thrive and multiply regardless of man's problems.

In 1582, Antonio de Espejo led a group of men north in an attempt to determine the fate of Franciscans who, under Fray Augustin de Rodriguez, had vanished on a missionary venture the previous year.

Espejo found that the friars had been killed, apparently by Zuni. But instead of turning back, he pushed on—possibly as far north as the present site of Jerome, Arizona.

Then, in 1598, Juan de Oñate, with soldiers, monks, and colonists, established a settlement near what is now Santa Fe, New Mexico.

The Pueblo Rebellion of 1680 drove out the settlers who had taken up life in this new land, but by 1692 colonists began to return to this area of the South-

Coronado and his army came to the New World seeking treasures; they departed empty-handed, leaving behind cattle and horses

west. Meanwhile, in 1690, the Spaniards had established a mission in Texas, near the Louisiana border, to enable Spanish missionaries to preach to the Indians. This mission, like others that followed in increasing number after 1716, was stocked with cattle. These cattle were direct descendents of the original Spanish cattle that made the trip with Columbus. So quickly did they multiply on the ranch-missions that by 1770 some 40,000 head were reported on one mission alone—the Espiritu Santo.

More men, horses, and cattle moved north across the Rio Grande. The missions increased in size and number; each had a large herd of cattle. Mexican settlers found the country inviting, the water plentiful, and the grass nourishing for their stock. Soon the country across the Rio Grande was dotted with ranches, and great herds of cattle wandered loose. Missions and colonies were also established along the Pacific and Gulf coasts.

Except for the animals that were to be consumed as food or killed for their hides, there was no market for the cattle, and the increase in the size of the herds far exceeded the demand. There were therefore thousands of cattle roaming the country. These animals, descendants of abandoned herds or runaways from carelessly run ranches, came to be as wild as the buffalo. They developed extraordinary stamina and skill, and were very difficult to round up. Many new-comers, in fact, assumed that they were really "wild" cattle and native to the country.

As the cattle herds of the missions and colonists continued to grow, it became increasingly important to keep them under control. Gradually it became the practice to hire men for tending cattle—men who showed special skills at riding and handling horses. These riders were called vaqueros, and they can be said to have been the first cowboys. Until 1821, when the first American colonists began to drift into Texas, these vaqueros were Mexican.

The American pioneers began to settle among the Mexicans, to collect cattle in the Mexican manner, and to establish ranches of their own. The number of cattle in Texas continued to increase rapidly, and it has been said that at least 100,000 head were there in 1830. The rapid build-up began to be felt on every ranch, and it soon became plain that a market for these cattle had to be found.

Finally, in 1842, some cattle were driven from Texas to New Orleans, and by the 1850s work stock and beef herds had reached Arkansas, California, Illinois, Iowa, Missouri, Ohio, and Oklahoma. Even New York got a look at the long-horned Texas cattle, one group having been shipped in from Indiana by rail in 1854.

The turning point of the early cattle drive efforts was the California Gold Rush. In 1848, gold was discovered at Sutter's Mill, and thousands of men headed west. For the Texas rancher this meant great numbers of consumers for beef, greater numbers than could be supplied by the cattle then in California.

Despite the danger of raids by hostile Indians and the difficulties of driving cattle across wild country, the California market became an important one for Texas cattle, and remained so up to the start of the Civil War.

Shipping cattle east, however, created even more serious problems. Texas cattle carried a tick on their bodies which, while it did not affect them, brought sickness and death to the less hardy cattle in Missouri and other states. The ranchers in these areas knew only that the Texas longhorns gave their cattle "Texas fever," and strong action was taken to keep the longhorns in Texas. Armed men met the cowboys at the border and turned them back at gunpoint. State laws were passed denying entry to Texas cattle, and though efforts were partially successful in bypassing the guarded border points and thus evading the new laws, the cutoff was quite effective, and the drives were sharply checked.

With most of the newly found markets now out of reach, the cattle were bottled up in Texas again. By

The first cowboys were Mexican riders called vaqueros

The cowboy's horse was of Spanish origin; it was small, tough, and fast

1860, the number of cattle in the state had climbed to at least 4,500,000.

This situation continued until the outbreak of the Civil War. Then, suddenly, virtually every able-bodied cowboy and rancher went off to war. Behind them, untended, were the 4,500,000 cattle.

When the war began, trail driving came to a halt. When the cowboy returned to Texas four years later, the number of cattle had risen to at least 6,000,000, and probably more.

Texas, like most of the South after the war, was poor. The only thing it had was cattle, but they were worthless without a market. Many farms were in bad shape due to neglect; money was scarce; and the cattle were everywhere. The North, however, was strong economically, and in a buying mood. Furthermore, it was short on beef and needed cattle to stock the ranges.

Here, then, was Texas bursting at the seams with millions of longhorn cattle, and the northern states with hardly a cow in sight. It was clear that the only salvation was to get the cattle to market. Since there were no railroads connecting these two great areas, there was only one thing to do: walk the cattle out of Texas. In 1866, the first herds moved north across the Red River.

The era of the cowboy had begun. Fact and fancy

began to mingle almost at once in the public mind. But whether the cowboy was a knight-errant or simply a man who did a tough job well, one thing is clear: the job could not have been done without him. Before describing his job, both off and on the trail, let us first take a closer look at the man—what he wore and why, and what he rode.

2 · Clothes, Guns, and Horses

❁

THE COWBOY had a style of dress uniquely suited to his way of life. Though his outward appearance might seem flamboyant to the stranger, every article of clothing was essential in his work. The extent to which he decorated his clothes and the money he chose to spend on them reflected his personal idiosyncracies and individual pride.

The cowboy usually spent a considerable amount of money on his clothes and saddle gear. This was one of the few pleasures allowed him. His work was hard, dirty, tiring, and seemingly endless. There were no days off on the roundups and trail drives, and no regular hours. His relaxation came at the end of the trail in the cow towns or between duties on the home ranch.

The cowboy coming in from the trail after a long, hard ride, and with several months pay in his shirt pocket, wanted to show off a little. One of the first things he did was to buy himself a new outfit. If the man was an old-time cowhand, he wanted an outfit that would set him off from those with less time in the saddle. And no one wanted to look like a beginner, new to the range.

The "tenderfoot" could be spotted easily. Knowing the range only from dime novels or romanticized newspaper accounts, he would arrive ready for work with laced boots and a silk shirt. Naturally, the old hands would make fun of him until he exchanged his fancy duds for something more practical and modest. The young man, now dressed for work and not show, could buy a pony and saddle in the early days for twenty-five dollars. Another fifteen would go for leather chaps, a hat, and saddle blankets. A pistol could be bought for about twelve dollars.

The cowboy "code" did, however, allow the experienced hand to splurge his hard-earned cash on a fancy outfit if he wanted to, without fear of ridicule. It was possible to spend as much as five hundred dollars on a rig, which would include inlaid silver on his saddle, a silver-mounted bridle for his horse, and silver-mounted spurs for his custom-made boots. He could have gold trim on his hat, thick goat's wool on his chaps, and a pearl handle on his Colt .45.

But, as a rule, even the most weather-beaten,

saddle-wedded puncher was seldom this lavish. Fancy shirts or gaudy accessories were out of place and impractical on the range. A reasonably fine yet serviceable outfit could be had for under two hundred and fifty dollars, including a sixty dollar saddle.

The basic cowboy outfit did not change much with time. Styles changed, of course, as they do today, largely due to "fads." Changes came also as a result of differences in climate or the nature of the country, as well as the cowboy's desire to be identified with a part of the range country by the clothes that he wore. It's been said that one could tell a man's home base— whether he worked on the southwestern or northwestern range—by looking at his hat.

Three types of hats were popular at various times: the Mexican sombrero, the Stetson, and the broad-brimmed soft felt hat. The sombrero was a high-crowned hat with an embroidered, up-turned brim. Its cost, depending on the trim, might run as high as fifty dollars.

The Stetsons had crowns, or tops, that were up to eight inches high and brims wide enough to give good shade at high noon. The brims were often decorated with silk braid or with holes punched around the edges so that a piece of leather could be wound through to provide both stiffness and decoration. Generally the crown was dented around the sides if worn by a Texas cowboy, but left smooth sided, with the top pleated or folded down low, if the wearer came from the Northwest. A band of leather circled the base of the crown. Sometimes this leather band would be studded with silver. The cowboys of Arizona and New Mexico were known to substitute the skin of a rattlesnake for the regular band. If the wearer was a Texan, the band would often be of gold or silver wire.

Brim widths, too, were different, depending upon where the cowboy was from. Wide brims were favored in the Southwest, where protection from the sun was more important, while the Northwest cowboy kept his brim narrow to present less of a sail to the wind.

Whatever the variety, hats performed important jobs. With the brims turned up they served as drinking cups if nothing else was around. They could be used to fan campfires into life and chase mosquitoes. Wide brims could be pulled way down and tied over the ears as protection against the cold. They also protected the rider against the wind, rain, blazing hot sun, and clouds of sand.

The cowboy was never without his neckerchief or bandanna. This was a large piece of cloth folded over several times to form a triangle and tied around his neck. The drag riders—cowboys who rode behind the cattle in a trail drive—protected themselves from the dust by pulling their bandannas up over the lower half of their faces.

The "wipes," as the puncher called his neckerchief, was usually worn with the knot at the back and the fold hanging down over his chest. On a hot day, with the sun slanting from behind, it would be reversed so that the cloth would protect his neck.

The neckerchief was usually made of cotton, although silk was not unknown. Some neckerchiefs were black or blue in color, but red was the favorite. White was never worn, simply because it showed the dirt too fast.

The cowboy wore a loose-fitting flannel shirt, open at the neck, and in the early days, woolen pants. Later, Levis became popular, but never denim coveralls, which were considered the outfit of a farmer.

Chaps, or "leggins," were worn by all cowboys when on the range. They were usually made of leather and were open at the seat. They extended down the front and side of each leg to provide full protection when riding through brush and cactus country. In the Southwest chaps were generally smooth and without much adornment. A calfskin pair sold for about nine dollars. In the Northwest they were usually made from animal skins with the hair left on for added protection against the cold, and a pair of good ones would run up to twenty dollars.

The cowboy's dress consisted of a loose-fitting flannel shirt, woolen pants, chaps, boots, gloves, neckerchief, a broad-brimmed hat, and a vest

The cowboy's boots were a source of great pride to him. They were made of the finest leather and handsomely decorated around the tops. The boots came up to just below the knee, with heels about two inches high, and thin, narrow soles. The thin sole gave the rider the "feel" of the stirrup, and the high heel kept his foot from slipping. Vanity takes different forms at different times, but the cowboy's weak spot was the size of his feet. For his own reasons, he wanted people to think his feet were small, and he squeezed himself into the smallest boot size he could stand.

Spurs, or "grappling irons," were worn most of the time. They were most useful in roundup work. The rider did not use them to hurt or punish the horse, but to make him move quickly, whether this be turning, stopping, or starting.

Most spurs were ornate in design, and the cowboy took great pride in owning a beautiful pair. Among the many different types were big roweled spurs with bells, and hand-forged, silver-inlaid types with droop shanks and small rowels. Sizes and designs varied with individual preference, but all made quite a noise when the cowboy walked along a wooden sidewalk or entered a room.

Gloves were standard throughout the year. The most commonly worn were of fine buckskin. Gloves offered warmth in the winter and protection from rope burn in the summer.

Deep cuffed or gauntleted gloves were the most popular, as they gave protection to the wrists. The gauntlet, which was part of the glove, was about five inches deep and usually embroidered. Cuffs were separate from the gloves themselves and were fastened about the wrist with snaps or buckles.

The cowboy also had a raincoat—a yellow slicker similar to the type fishermen wear. He always wore a vest, mostly because of the extra pockets it gave him. Nearly every man owned an extra fancy and colorful vest for special trips into town for celebrations or dances. It was made of wool and dyed a bright, solid color.

The saddle was the most valuable piece of gear that the cowboy owned, and he paid a great deal of money to get the very best. Not only did saddles have to be comfortable, they had to be ruggedly built as well. They weighed as much as forty pounds and were made of leather-covered wood. The pommel, or "horn," was of forged steel covered with leather. Costs ran as high as a hundred and fifty dollars for a fine silver-buckled saddle with intricate designs tooled into the leather. An ordinary one could, however, be bought for about forty dollars.

The saddle was fastened to the horse with "cinches,"

or leather straps running under the horse's belly from one side of the saddle to the other. A saddle with one cinch was called a "center-fire"; a two-cinch saddle was called a "double-fire," or "double-barreled," saddle.

In the early days on the range, a cowboy was never without his gun. Later, as the threat of Indian raids and other hazards disappeared, the gun went out of fashion, except for show.

The Colt revolver, using a .45 caliber metallic cartridge, was the favorite, but before this came into regular use many men carried "horse pistols"—single-shot weapons. The drawbacks to this gun were many, but the chief difficulty was the necessity of reloading after every shot.

In 1836, Samuel Colt developed a repeating gun, or revolver, for men serving in the Texas Navy. Later, some of these guns found their way into the hands of the Texas Rangers. In 1844, a party of fifteen Rangers came upon a war party of eighty mounted Comanches spoiling for a fight. The warriors, confident of victory against a small party of men armed with single-shot guns, taunted the Rangers to come and fight. The Indians had never seen "repeating" guns, and in the battle that followed, half of the startled Indians were killed, and the rest fled. From then on, the Colt revolver fast became the standard gun of the West.

The early Colt, like the Remington-Beals Army re-volver, held self-consuming combustible cartridges and was muzzle loaded. To load it, one had to remove the cylinder and load the cartridges in the front, then ram them home with a lever attached to the bottom of the barrel. While these revolvers were a revolu-tionary advance over previous weapons, they were not trouble free. Sometimes when they were fired, the flash from one cylinder would ignite the powder in the next, so that all five or six cartridges exploded at once, demolishing the weapon.

The cowboy never wore two six-shooters. The most he ever carried was one pistol and one rifle. The "two-gun" men were the outlaws and the marshals.

The cowboy's horse was small, tough, and fast. Like the longhorn cattle, it was of Spanish origin and had evolved into an animal suited to the range. In *The Story of the Cowboy*, written in 1897, Emerson Hough commented on the Spanish pony: "For gen-eration after generation it lost flesh and gained angles, lost beauty and gained 'wind' and stomach and bot-tom and speed, until at the time of the first American cowboy's meeting with it, it was a small, hardy, wiry, untamed brute, as wild as a hawk, as fleet as a deer, as strong as an ox."

These horses turned quickly and easily, good quali-ties for roundup work. They weighed no more than

600 pounds as a rule, and could travel fast and far. They were remarkably strong and could withstand great punishment. Sometimes the cowboy would have to ride his horse until the animal was exhausted, but the very next morning the horse would be full of spirit, and would show it by trying to throw his rider off as the first act of the day.

Some of the horses were never really tamed. Theodore Roosevelt, in his book *Ranch Life and the Hunting Trail*, notes that many of his horses "have to this day [1888] traits not likely to set a timid or a clumsy rider at his ease. One or two run away and cannot be held by even the strongest bit; others can hardly be bridled or saddled until they have been thrown; two or three have a tendency to fall over backward; and half of them buck more or less, some so hard that only an expert can sit them; several I never ride myself, save from dire necessity."

The cowboy rode only male horses or geldings; never a mare. In the Southwest, the horse was called a cow horse or cow pony; on the northern ranges it was a "cayuse." Bronchos were wild, or "bad," horses, and as Theodore Roosevelt suggested, they caused a great deal of trouble.

As time went on, many ranchmen began to hire men to break the broncs. These men became quite skilled —some of them became famous for their work—and

Bronco busting required skill and patience

the profession known as bronco busting came into being.

Generally, the cowboy did not provide his own horse when doing roundup or trail work. He was given use of from seven to ten horses by the man who hired him. The only things the cowboy carried with him were his saddle and personal gear. He took good care of his string of horses, however, and these mounts were his to ride until the work was over.

3 · Ranch and Range

✲

THE COWBOY spent most of the winter months on a ranch. If the weather behaved itself, these months were reasonably pleasant, and the work—with the exception of calf branding which was done in the early spring, when the snow began to melt—was not too hard.

If the winter was one of many storms and deep snows, the work was fearfully difficult, for the men had to ride out to keep close watch on the cattle. If an animal was found lying in the snow, it had to be forced to stand or it would soon freeze to death. The surest method of getting a half frozen, half starved cow to stand on its feet was to "tail him up." A cowboy would take hold of the animal's tail and twist it with all his force, until the sheer pain made the cow jump to its feet. It was not a job the cowboy looked forward to, but it kept many a cow on its feet while being led to a place where shallow snow could be cleared to expose the grass needed for food.

During a storm the cattle drifted in the direction the wind was blowing. Many times this put them many miles off their range by the time the storm lost its punch, and the cowboys had to drive them back again. There were times, however, when they would be dead by the time the men found them. Often they drifted until they came to a blind canyon. They then stood huddled together until they dropped one by one.

In good weather and bad there was "outriding" and "line riding" to be done. When outriding, the cowboy roamed far and wide over the range to spot his cattle and to look over the grass and water supply situation. If necessary, the men would move the cattle to a spot that offered better protection against storms or to one that was more abundant in grass and water.

The riders kept on the watch for straying animals and for signs of wolves and rustlers. Occasionally they had the job of pulling a helpless calf or cow from a bog or tending to a newborn calf unable to take care of itself because of severe weather.

The "line rider's" job was to keep watch along the ranch's range boundary line. Two cowboys might work out from each of a number of "line camps"

Two line riders generally worked out of each line camp, posted along a ranch's boundary

The fence riders checked and repaired broken sections of fence along the boundary line

posted along the ranch's boundary. In the mornings they would head along the line in opposite directions, riding until, at the point halfway to the next camp, each would meet another rider, coming in the other direction. They would stop awhile, exchange gossip and stories, and turn about for the return trip.

Later, when wire fences came into wide use on the range, the line rider became a fence rider, checking to make sure that the fences were not broken or cut, and repairing them if they were damaged.

There was also work to be done around the ranch, though the old-time cowboy felt this was beneath him and let his feelings be known. Supplies had to be purchased in town; the well might need tending; work horses had to be shod and wood chopped, gathered, and brought into camp. Wagons had to be repaired, horses broken, and saddles, lariats, and harnesses mended.

If there was a woman at the ranch, she did the best she could to keep it neat and clean, but the odds were against her. The main ranch house was usually made of logs, particularly in the early days, with the spaces between filled with sticks and mud. Frontier workmanship seldom succeeded in keeping the dust outside where it belonged.

The inside of the ranch house was simple and uncluttered, with the invaluable fireplace, a large table,

and a few chairs. On some ranches the cowboys slept
in bunks that lined the walls of the house, while on
others there were separate quarters for the men. On
the northern plains the stove was in the main ranch
house, and the cook prepared and served the meals
there. In the warmer areas to the south, there was usually a separate cook house.

Joseph G. McCoy has written that the cowboy's
daily fare consisted of "corn bread, mast-fed bacon
and coffee . . . occasionally they have fresh beef and
less often they have vegetables of any description.
They do their own cooking in the rudest and fewest
possible vessels, often not having a single plate or
knife and fork other than their pocket knife, but
gather around the camp kettle in true Indian style,
and with a piece of bread in one hand proceed to fish
up a piece of 'sow belly' and dine sumptuously, not
forgetting to stow away one or more quarts of the
strongest coffee imaginable, without sugar or cream,
indeed you would hesitate . . . to call it coffee or ink."

McCoy was describing a meal on the range during
the very early days of trail driving, when there was
no chuck wagon, and the men carried and cooked
their own food. Though such improvements as a cook
to prepare the food on the range and at the ranch
house made this side of the cowboy's life easier, the
basic diet did not change greatly, and McCoy's de-

scription of the coffee has been confirmed many times over. As Edward Everett Dale of the University of Oklahoma noted in his book *Frontier Ways*, "the cook firmly believed that there is no such thing as strong coffee but only 'weak people.'"

During the Civil War coffee was seldom available on the western ranges, and many substitutes were used. These included rye, corn, wheat, okra seeds, roasted acorns, and sweet potatoes. Honey and molasses often took the place of sugar. Other items in short supply due to the war included soap, matches, and cloth.

In time the food and its variety improved. The cooks rarely provided much in the way of a dessert beyond dried fruit, sometimes topped with syrup, but they could make a stew that the men never seemed to tire of. Called "son-of-a-gun" stew when in polite company, the stew was made with beef heart, liver, tongue, marrow gut, sweetbreads, brains, and pieces of tenderloin.

The cowboy liked his meat fried rather than broiled, and he often dipped his chunks of meat in a thick pan gravy called "sop." He rarely ate lamb, and considered it an insult when offered it. Milk, butter, eggs, and potatoes were rarely found on the range.

The cook was paid more than the cowboys, and a good man was well worth it.

Ranch houses were simple and uncluttered

There was not much in the way of reading material at a ranch, unless the owner happened to be an educated man. With rare exceptions, the cowboy was uneducated and unmarried. In the evening hours the men were content to talk, roll their cigarettes, play cards, and thumb through well-worn magazines. Liquor was never seen on the range, and the ranch that had some to offer was almost as rare.

To break the monotony of ranch life, the cowboys often went hunting. Before the range was swept clean of buffalo the men loved to ride out in search of a buffalo calf to rope.

Emerson Hough described an early hunt for buffalo calves in the Texas Panhandle. He and his men got thirteen calves, "with much of the roping done by a cowboy not yet twenty years of age, who was very skillful in his calling, and an especially fine roper."

Hough recalled that "often the buffalo cow would charge the man thus taking liberties with her calf. . . . The cowboy did not like to release his calf after the pains of the long run, and he did not like to lose his horse on the horns of the enraged cow, which pursued him steadily and viciously. There was sure to be a constricted but exciting chase about a narrow circle, with the rope as its radius and the calf as the pivotal point. In two instances it was necessary to kill the cow to save the cowboy from death or serious injury."

The cowboys also hunted grizzly bear, antelope, deer, elk, and mountain lion, when and if they could be found. The grizzly was especially dangerous because of its size and strength, and it was never chased alone. Usually a number of cowboys rode the grizzly down, each throwing his rope to get the great beast hopelessly tangled and trussed up on the ground.

Wolves were more commonly hunted, for they preyed upon the livestock and often inflicted heavy losses. Bounty was sometimes offered for wolf scalp; the amount ranged from ten dollars to twenty dollars —enough, one old-timer said, "to keep us in chewing tobacco for a month or two." Some ranchers kept specially trained dogs—greyhounds were a favorite—to track and bring down the tough wolf.

The cowboys also had an occasional opportunity to go to dances in town. When these dances were held, men came from twenty miles and more around. Although the women were outnumbered by the cowboys ten to one, this did not dampen anyone's spirits. The dances were usually great successes, and the cowboys looked forward to them. They would deck themselves out in their best clothes, clean up their boots, get their hair trimmed, tuck their pants legs into boot tops, and shine up their spurs.

The cowboys loved dancing, although most of them were not good at it, and the dancing usually went on until dawn. Because of the shortage of women, many of the cowboys had to dance with each other. The fiddler worked hard; the caller kept a dizzy pace; spurs jangled; and the men drank their bourbon whisky. The resulting bedlam could be heard for a mile around on a clear night.

When dawn came, the men began to break away for the ride back to the home ranch to resume their daily work.

These social events were far different from what the cowboy came up against in the cow towns at the end of the trails. Towns like Abilene and Dodge spared little in their efforts to fleece every last dime from the cowboy fresh off the trail. Into these towns came the dregs of society—gamblers, desperadoes, and prostitutes—and their target was the cowboy. Many a man left the town the morning following his arrival minus his hard-earned pay.

The cowboys could not be blamed for wanting to "cut loose" after a long drive. Often when they were on the trail they did not see a face other than that of a fellow cowboy, for months. They were eager to wash away the dirt of the range, to buy a new set of clothes, to eat a meal at a table, to try their hand at gambling, dancing, and drinking. They rode into Dodge and other cow towns looking for excitement, and they were rarely disappointed.

The dances held at or near the home ranch were by contrast polite and quiet affairs. The women were the

Hunting grizzly bears was a dangerous sport that broke the monotony of the winter months

The shortage of women often made it necessary for the cowboys to dance with each other at their parties

wives and daughters of local men and were quite a different type from those found in the dance halls.

Besides the infrequent dances for the ranch-bound cowboys, there were horse races and tournaments. Sometimes cowboys from the different ranches raced each other over long courses. There were also endurance races, the longest probably being a 500-mile run from Deadwood, South Dakota, to Omaha, Nebraska, with a $1,000 prize presented to the winner by Buffalo Bill Cody.

Other games on horseback included picking up coins from the ground while going at a full gallop, and a 150-yard race gathering rings with a tapered lance. Spaced along the course for this race were upright posts fixed with crossbars, from which hung rings suspended by loose ropes. Out of a possible perfect catch of fifteen rings, eight or ten was considered good.

There were also bronco-busting and calf-roping contests. These began as local contests between a few men or between two rival ranches, but they were so popular that they spread to the towns. Prescott, Arizona, saw the first rodeo where prizes were awarded on July 4, 1888.

Emerson Hough recalled that one of the favorite amusements at a cow camp was to put a pair of tarantula spiders or snakes together to fight, with the cowboys making friendly bets on the outcome.

With the coming of spring, the cowboys had to get ready for the first roundup and the branding of the new calf crop. Ott Black, an old-time trail driver, claimed that branding was the hardest part of cowpunching. It was certainly one of the dirtiest and most tiresome jobs the cowboy had to do.

Brands were made up of letters, numbers, or signs —or combinations of all three—permanently burned into the skin of the calf to identify it as belonging to a particular rancher.

A typical branding crew consisted of "catch hands," "flankers," "iron men," and a "butcher," or "cutter," for earmarking or dewlapping if this was included as part of the owner's mark.

A "catch hand" would rope a calf, usually by the heels, and drag it behind his horse over to the waiting "flankers." The flankers would then grab the animal by one ear, clasp an arm on the same flank, and with a quick knee movement timed to the calf's jump, flip the animal up and out, so that it landed on its side. One flanker then held the calf's hind feet stretched out, while another put one knee on the animal's neck and the other on its back, while his hands held the upper foreleg doubled at the knee. In this way, the animal was powerless to move and was ready for the branding iron.

If the calf had to be earmarked—that is, have its ear slit with a knife—this was done at the same time as the branding. This was a messy job for the "cutter," for the calf, when finally allowed to rise, would usually throw or sling its head from side to side, splattering blood in all directions.

The noise of the bawling calves, the danger that a cow would suddenly dash to the rescue of her calf, the heat and dust, and the general confusion of the work made branding no pleasure for the men, and they were glad when it was finally over.

If cattle from several ranches were being gathered for a trail drive, they had to be "road branded" with a common brand for all, so that they could all be identified should the herds of more than one drive become mixed together while on the trail.

In early times, branding was done on the open range. Later it was done in a corral, and today most branding is done by running the calf through a narrow chute. A bar is placed in front of the animal, and when the animal stops, the hot branding iron is put on it through the side railings of the chute.

4 · The Roundup

✸

THE ROUNDUPS, which were held each spring and fall, were the most exciting and colorful of all the cowboy's duties. They were also the most demanding in terms of skill and stamina. In roundup work the cowboy was in the saddle for twelve to eighteen hours a day, with time off only to grab some grub and change to a fresh horse. He often slept out under the stars. A romantic thought, except that rain, mosquitoes, tarantulas, and assorted four-legged creatures—from Gila monsters to mountain lions—often interrupted the few hours sleep that he might have had.

For the most part, the cowboy looked forward to roundup work. Working far out on the range in the quiet hours just after dawn, either by himself or in company with a few other men, he knew the peace of the country, felt the sharpness of the cool morning air, and enjoyed the movement of a fine horse beneath him. On mornings like this he knew why he had chosen cow work as a way of life, and he would not have traded for any other job in the world.

At other times—times of wind and rain and precious little sleep—he might have second thoughts.

Before fences were put up to mark the boundaries of the ranches, the prairie was free and wide open to everyone. Most cattlemen owned relatively small parcels of land, regardless of the size of their cattle herds; the famous and immense ranch spreads came later.

The cattlemen turned their herds loose upon the open range to graze and water and multiply the whole year around. The cattle were Texas longhorns, a breed long since replaced by fatter and meatier stock. The longhorns were a breed superior to any cattle then or now insofar as ruggedness, ingenuity, and the instinct for survival were concerned. They were neither the fattest nor the meatiest cattle a man could wish for, but they stood up under conditions that would scare a modern animal half to death.

The longhorns stayed out on the range right through the fierce winters, when the high winds swept the snow across the grass and the deep cold sealed the watering places. These cattle knew how to drift with a storm, how to find water where there seemed to be none; in short, how to sustain life in a land seemingly incapable of offering sustenance. In the spring, when

A calf had to be thrown on its side and tied securely before it could be branded

The cowboy looked forward to roundup time when he worked far out on the open range

the snows melted, the stream beds began to fill and the grass began to green, the tough longhorns would be found, gaunt and weak, but very much alive.

The idea of the roundup, whether in spring or fall, was to bring the cattle in from the far reaches of the range. The spring roundup was to gather all the calves that had been born during the winter and to brand them with their owners' marks. The spring gather was also to put all the cattle back on their home range, for over the long winter the cattle from all the ranches around would wander freely, mixing and drifting together.

The spring work generally started about the beginning of May and lasted for forty days or more. The starting date was not absolute; it depended primarily on the condition of the grass.

The fall roundup began near the first of September. It was also for the purpose of branding calves—those born since the spring and those which for one reason or another had been missed during the earlier roundup. The calves missed earlier were yearlings by the time the fall came.

The fall roundup had a larger purpose: the gathering of animals for shipment to the North for beef or range stock. In the early days this "shipment" meant a trail drive; later, after the trails were closed, the cattle went to Kansas and other points by rail.

The herds were made up of cattle contributed by each cattleman who had animals for sale. These might be all-beef herds—animals four or more years old. Often it was a mixed herd of beef, steers, and yearlings. Yearlings were between one and two years old, and steers between two and four.

Usually, a deal was made with a northern buyer for the delivery of a certain number of cattle. A drover —the man who took the herd up the trail—then contacted ranchers and made deals with them regarding the number of cattle they would include in the big herd. The drover paid the ranchers and then hired the cowboys to handle the herd on the trail. The ranchers made the necessary arrangements to put their cattle in the drover's hands. To do this, they rounded them up and moved them to a prearranged point on the prairie.

Roundups were quite simple in the early days. The number of cattle involved was small, and the territory to be covered was limited in size. The local ranchers worked together to round up the cattle in their area. The system was inefficient; many cattle were missed because not enough men could be sent out to permit careful working of the range. This problem became more intense as herds grew in size and the number of ranchers increased. Their cattle became mixed together and drifted great distances in winter. It was obvious that a more businesslike method had to be found.

The system that was finally adopted was the district roundup system. Under it, a vast grazing territory was divided up into roundup districts, each about 100 miles square, and each district was then divided into ranges. Each range took from three to eight days to cover during the roundup.

In the spring the ranchmen or their representatives would meet to work out the details for the district roundups in their territory. A roundup boss was selected to head the work in each district and to see that schedules were followed as the roundup proceeded from range to range.

Every rancher supplied cowboys and the horses for the remuda, or "saddle band"—the extra ponies needed for the roundup work. Strings of from six to eight or ten horses were supplied for each cowboy's use. If the ranch could afford it, there was a chuck wagon. The smaller ranches often pooled their resources, supplying fewer cowboys each and a common chuck wagon.

Three or four days before the roundup work began, the cowboys, with their remudas and chuck wagons, would start to arrive on the roundup ground. Clouds of dust hung over the area, which became alive with men and equipment milling everywhere. By the time the order was given to begin the work, there might be, if the roundup was big, at least twenty chuck wagons, 400 cowboys, and over 2,000 horses in camp.

A wait of several days was necessary to allow the men and wagons from the farthest ranches to reach the area. The wait was welcomed, for it meant a time of rest. It also meant a time for visiting, card playing, gossipping, singing, bronc busting, and horse racing. It was a time to greet men not seen since the last roundup. It was also a time when old grudges flared up, and the roundup bosses had their hands full keeping 400 tough men in check. It was a time for "telling windys"—farfetched tales—and each man tried to outdo the other; and a time for rolling cigarettes and enjoying all the company—something the cowboy would not have for long.

The night before the work began was the time for putting gear in order. A good night's sleep helped too, for at 3:00 A.M. or so the cook yelled "turn out," and the entire camp came alive.

As the men grabbed some meat, bread, and coffee at the chuck wagon, the horse wranglers, who tended the horses, were bringing up the remudas from where they had been held during the night. The men tossed down the second or third tin of coffee, picked their mounts, saddled up, and with a rush, swept out of camp by the hundreds, heading for their assigned positions on the range.

The cowboys were divided into groups, or squads,

each with its own boss. The groups reached their positions, sometimes fifteen or twenty miles from the camp, and the roundup began. The men farthest out rode the "outer circle" and were called "lead drive" men, while those in closer rode the "inner circle." All the men doing this work were called "circle riders."

Each man worked in toward the center of a circle, heading back toward the agreed-upon roundup ground. The men poked into every cut and ravine, and behind every hill. Riding circle was both tiring and dangerous. The cows had to be hunted and routed out of wild, rugged terrain, and the longhorn, long loose and as wild and clever as the deer, knew every hiding place, every bit of brush too thick for a man on horseback to enter. Often, a longhorn, flushed out of its cover, would make a wild dash across the prairie to escape, and it was the cowboy's job to chase the animal, overtake it, and encourage it along in the right direction. In country pockmarked with prairie dog holes and unseen cuts in the earth, a race across such ground could prove dangerous, and sometimes fatal.

Sometimes, while riding circle, a cowboy would come up against a cow that refused all attempts to move it toward the roundup ground. At such times the cowboy would try to rope it and tie it down. The cow, now helpless, would be left where it fell, to wait until the herd could be brought up to it. Then, when

After a hard day's work, the cowboys would head for the chuck wagon
where they would eat and relax

Great skill was required of the cowboy and his horse in
cutting out

the cow was cut loose, it would rise to find itself among its fellows, and it was usually content to move along without further trouble.

The work was slow, the heat intense, and the dust thicker. The idea was not speed but thoroughness. From the roundup ground great clouds of dust would become visible far out on the range as the groups of cattle were worked in closer. The circles were tightened; the separate cowboys and groups of men came within sight of each other; and large numbers of cows moved slowly forward. By the end of the roundup thousands of cattle had been packed into one big herd, raising enough noise and dust to satisfy any outdoor man.

In they came: calves, mavericks, steers—black, sandy, and in between; lowing and bellowing; shifting; sweeping their long horns and dragging their tails on the ground. Shaky looking calves; and big slab-sided, long-legged, and long-necked steers. They carried brands of every type; cows looked for their calves; and nearly all tried to figure out how they could make captivity as temporary as possible.

The cowboys would move their horses in close, scaring the cattle back into the herd if they tried to break. The cattle bawled; the cowboys yelled and whistled; the dust, the heat, and the smell of it all was memorable. The men who had been riding circle

—whether "in" or "out"—would dismount and pick another horse from the remuda.

The gather of cattle was held in close herd by a number of cowboys, while others, on their cutting horses, entered the herd to start the "work." Usually, three or four men did the cutting, or separating of the animals, at any one time.

At fall roundup time, there would be one cut for cows with unbranded calves, one cut for cows according to brand, and the beef cut. Each cut would be held away from the main herd being worked, to keep the cows from mingling together again before delivery. If the cowboys were cutting for the purpose of branding calves, the men would work the mother to the edge of the herd and then "dodge it out" onto the prairie. The calf would nearly always follow, and it would then be roped and dragged to the fire for branding with the same mark its mother bore.

If the men were cutting cattle for a drive, the animals would be cut into a beef herd, with more being added as the days passed, until the range had been covered and all the cattle needed had been thrown into this herd.

Cutting out was the most spectacular of cow work. Properly done, it was a beautiful thing to watch, and many a man proved himself a top hand in the eyes of his fellows when doing such work.

It took great skill to work a herd. The cowboy had to be a superior rider and his horse had to be the finest available. Cutting horses were noted for their quick movements and instant response to the commands of their riders. Ideally, the cutting horse was about fifteen hands high and strongly built.

It has been said that a good cutting horse, once he understood which cow or steer his rider was after, would do the job with little guidance. In such circumstances, the cowboy would let the reins lay loose on the horse's back and just hold on. The horse had to be gentle yet firm, and he had to know how to pick his way through the herd without upsetting the cattle. Like a hound in pursuit of a fox or rabbit, the horse would pursue his quarry and rarely lose the contest.

Once the cow had been spotted, the horse would make a quick dash at it and head it toward the side of the herd. If the cow tried to dodge the horse, the horse dodged with it, always staying between it and the rest of the herd. He would play his forefeet at the cow, urging it on if it faltered, and keeping in close behind. If, when the cow broke clear of the herd, it made a dash for freedom, the horse would be off like lightning to head it off and turn it back toward the cut.

The cowboy had to be quick witted himself. The sudden turnings of his horse could easily toss the rider

if he was not careful, and at times a big steer, un-
happy at the turn of events, would try to hook the
horse with its horns. When the cow grew weary of
trying to re-enter the herd it would move off toward
the cut, the cutting horse "walking on its heels" in
case it got any other contrary ideas, until another
cowboy took over the job of guiding it into the cut.
The cutting horse would then move back into the
herd, and the whole job would begin again.

If one of the big steers broke out of the herd, several cowboys would usually go after it. There were
many techniques for roping these big, dangerous animals. The most important element in roping was
timing. The cowboy would take off after the animal,
and when in position, start his lariat swinging above
his head. At the right moment, he would send the
loop on its way. Sometimes he hit for the horns, and
at other times he tried to catch the animal by the
legs. The moment the lariat settled on target, the cowboy jerked it tight. If the man was a Texan, the end
of his lariat was tied fast around the horn of his saddle; if he was from California or the northern states,
he looped the lariat around the horn, ready to turn it
free if trouble came.

At the moment the lariat was jerked tight around
some part of the steer, the cowboy's horse suddenly
stopped short, stiffened his front legs, and squatted,

digging in. If the steer tumbled to the right or left, the pony pivoted with it, always facing it. In this way the lariat would remain taut, and the cowboy could leap from his horse and tie the steer securely.

Another method of "throwing" a running animal— this time without the aid of the lariat—was for the cowboy to come alongside the animal, reach over and grab its tail, twist it around the saddle horn, and then have his pony cut suddenly to the side and away from the direction the animal was moving. Almost without fail, the animal would go down with a grunt in a cloud of dust, the wind knocked out of it.

The task of cutting out continued until all the cattle were divided up into smaller herds. The work went on day after day, and as one range was finished, another was started, and the smaller herds continued to grow until each might number several thousand cattle. Each day the work was basically the same: circle riding a range; throwing the cattle into the main herd; cutting, branding, and "holding" the cows and calves bearing one brand; cutting and holding the beef cattle; and after that range was worked, moving to the next, bringing all the individual herds along.

As the home range of one of the cut herds was reached, the cattle were turned loose again to graze on the land until the next roundup time. Slowly the roundup moved along, picking up cattle and leaving

Timing was the most important element in roping a steer

some, until the entire district was worked and all the animals were back where they belonged. The beef herd, however, was kept together for delivery to the spot where the drover would take it up the trail.

5 · The Trail Drive

WHILE ROUNDUP WORK held great excitement for the cowboy, the trail drive was the heart of the cattle industry and the most important part of a cowboy's job. The work was far different from that of the roundup. The herd moved slowly, and the drive, covering many hundreds of miles, took from three to six months, depending upon the destination. Yet few of the men wanted to remain behind on the ranch.

Trail work was hard and tiresome; it was lonely and dirty; and the cowboy's pay was hardly enough to make the work worth the effort. Yet year after year the cowboys went up the trail, and when they reached Kansas or other points at the end of the line, they turned around and came back to Texas to begin all over again the following season. They sometimes complained, cussed about the grub, and swore that some day they would retire to "the good life." But during the long winters of relative calm and inactivity, the cowboy was a restless man, itching to get back on a horse where he belonged, and he spent much of his leisure time talking about his experiences on the trail in seasons past.

The young boy, when he dreamed of some day being a cowboy, dreamed of going up the trail. So, too, the old-timer, thinking back over his past, thought mostly of his days on the trail, even though his job had involved much more than that.

The cowboy was happiest on the trail because it was a time of almost complete freedom and independence. In company with a small handful of men, he moved slowly across great expanses of prairie far away from civilization. In his view were great mountain ranges, hazy in the heat and dust of midday, sharp in the pure air of early morning. He sometimes rode for hours at a time without speaking, except to himself or to his horse. Generally an uneducated man, he nevertheless knew all there was to know about cow work, and he could be trusted to carry out this work faithfully regardless of the hardships on the trail.

The trail outfit was composed of about eleven men, the actual number depending upon the size of the trail herd. An eleven-man outfit would be made up of two "point" men, who rode in the lead, two "swing" men, two on the flank, and two "drag" men. Then there was the boss, the cook, and the horse wrangler.

One of the point men rode at the right front corner of the herd; the other point man rode the opposite lead position. These men set the pace and directed the forward movement of the herd, which was spread out up to two miles behind them.

Strung out behind the pointers on both sides of the herd were the swing and flank men. It was their job to keep the cattle from wandering away from the herd and to keep the animals from stopping or trying to turn back.

The drag men came last. This was often a thankless assignment, since they rode along in the dust made by the herd, and their job was to keep the stragglers—the weak and tired cattle—moving along. On very hot and dry days when the dust was thickest, the trail boss would rotate his men so that none of them had to eat dust for too long a time.

The ideal size for a herd was around 2,000 head. Herds considerably larger than this are recorded. In 1879, twelve men, including boss, cook, and wrangler, trailed 5,500 head from Texas to Sidney Bridge, Nebraska, on the North Platte River; in 1881, a herd of 6,500 was moved at one time, from Ogallala, Nebraska, to Belle Fourche, Wyoming, a distance of 600 miles; and in 1884, 5,533 head of cattle were trailed from Dodge City to Horse Creek, Wyoming.

Unless a herd was made up of cattle belonging to one owner, and therefore carried a common brand, the first job the cowboy had was to help in road branding. Every cow had to be marked with this brand. When this work was done, the herd could be started.

It was found best to drive the herd hard for the first couple days, thus covering twenty-five or thirty miles quickly. This tired the cattle so that they could be handled more easily and would rest at night; it also got them out of their home range in a hurry—an advantage, since they were easier to control in unfamiliar territory; and finally, it got them accustomed to being driven. After this initial period they were slowed down to the normal rate of from eight to ten miles a day.

After a few weeks on the trail, the herd would become "trail broke," and would be quite easy to handle if nothing out of the ordinary disturbed the animals. Usually, one of the animals would automatically assume the lead position in the herd and would remain there throughout the drive. The other cattle also had their preferred positions in the herd, and no matter how scrambled they might become while bedding down for the night, they would always jockey to find their rightful places when the drive began the next morning.

A day's drive would begin early in the morning, usually when the sun came up. The herd would be allowed to feed along for two or three miles and then be turned onto the trail. At midday, the herd would be turned off the trail again, to graze, and the men would eat lunch and rest. The drive would begin again in about an hour's time. The herd would then be driven until sundown, when, the "bed ground". reached, the cattle would be moved off the trail to eat their big meal. With this done, they would stand idly about chewing their cud and then, one by one, settle down to sleep.

At eleven or twelve o'clock the herd, in one body, would rise, shake itself, shift a bit, and then, with a tremendous sigh, settle down to earth to sleep. At dawn the animals would be up on their feet for another day's drive. If there was dew on the grass, they would move along without snipping at the grass until the sun had dried off the dew.

Though much of the drive was uneventful and quiet, it was not without problems. Storms were frequent; there were great stretches where water was unavailable; Indians made their presence felt; swollen rivers had to be crossed; and the cattle might stampede at the drop of a hat.

The most important thing was to keep the herd quiet and moving at a steady pace. If the cattle ran, they ran off "tallow," or fat. If they were not bothered by anything, there was a good chance they would not become unruly. The movie scenes showing a herd surrounded by whooping, shooting cowboys are simply not true, for if such a thing was ever attempted, the cattle would be certain to stampede.

At night there were four watches. The cowboys, in turn, slowly circled the herd, talking and singing to it, for the cattle seemed to be comforted by the sound of a human voice. The men had to be always on guard for any sign of trouble. Sometimes it would come from a steer that seemed bent on stirring up the others; sometimes the snap of a twig, the movement of a jack rabbit; the flare of a match, or a strange smell. Whatever it was, it would bring every animal to its feet, and the herd would be off and running.

The stampede was a frightening experience. With a great, thunderous noise, the cattle would rush through the pitch blackness, their horns rattling against one another's, their hocks clattering, the dust rising in thick clouds, and the ground trembling from the pounding of thousands of hoofs.

With the first sounds of trouble, every cowboy in the camp was up and racing for his horse. The cowboys' first objective was to overtake the leaders of the stampede and turn them from their course. In this way, the leaders would gradually be brought around full-circle and meet the tail end of the stampede. By turning the leaders inward, the cowboys would wind the herd in upon itself like a spring. Eventually the

A trail drive took the cowboy across great expanses of open prairie, far from civilization

To stop a stampede, the cowboys would have to over-take the lead cattle and turn them from their course

herd would jam up tight, with the all-important lead cattle caught in dead center and unable to move. This way of stopping a stampede was called "milling," or "ring herding."

Many times the cattle could not be turned, no matter what the men did. On these occasions the herd just kept running, sometimes all night long. When it stopped at last, it might be many miles off the trail, its members scattered in every direction. For the cowboy, this meant that the animals had to be rounded up and thrown back on the trail once again—a job that might take several days.

For the cowboys trying to halt a stampede, danger was everywhere. In the darkness and dust they could not see the ground, nor more than a few of the closest cattle. The rider usually had no idea where the other riders were; they might be riding with him or he might be all alone.

The prairie was marked with cuts and gullies, dried stream beds, and prairie dog holes. Even in daylight, riding over such land could be risky business; but at night, during a stampede, it was a hair-raising experience. If a rider went down while riding close to the herd, his fate was sealed unless he had a barrelful of luck.

One range practice during a stampede was for the cowboys to call out or yell; in this way the men would know if their partners were all right. If one of the voices stopped suddenly, the men would know that something had happened.

Many things could cause cattle to stampede, but nothing terrified them more than a storm. The western states are hit by storms that are usually violent and sudden, and at certain times of the year the thunder and lightning storms are particularly ferocious.

Some of the worst electrical and hail storms occur in north and central Texas. Many men have described the manner in which the lightning seems to settle and creep along the ground. Men, horses, and cattle were often killed by bolts of lightning.

One trail driver, recalling a lightning storm in Nebraska, spoke of flash, forked, chain, and blue lightning, and ball lightning, which rolled along the ground. The air smelled of burning sulphur, and the lightning could be seen dancing on the horns of the cattle, the ears of the horses, and the brims of the cowboys' hats.

Another cowboy, recalling such storms, said that little balls of lightning—"about the size of a pea"— could be seen on the horses' ears and the men's mustaches.

On one of the banks of the Red River in 1878, a lightning bolt struck in the midst of a herd, killing nine cattle and setting off a stampede.

One trail driver, during his second night up the

trail from Dime Box, Texas, with 1,400 head of cattle, was hit by a violent storm shortly after bedding down the herd for the night. The cattle ran all night.

Once, at the bank of the Red River, ten or fifteen herds of cattle and two or three herds of horses were being held from crossing because of high water. That night a wild storm broke, scattering animals in every direction, despite the efforts of more than 300 cowboys. The next day 30,000 cattle and several thousand horses were mixed together in one gigantic herd. It was ten days before the herds were separated again.

In the winter the blizzards caused the trouble. During one storm on record 1,600 cattle drifted into the North Platte River. Of this number 400, mostly yearlings, were drowned.

E. C. Abbott, in his book *We Pointed Them North*, notes that once during a wild snowstorm, the cowboys' horses had to be led back and forth in front of a row of fires all night to keep them from freezing to death. However, on another night, other cowboys were not so fortunate. During a blizzard, in Indian territory, every horse went down—frozen to death— with his rider still aboard. In addition, sixty-five horses —the entire balance of the outfit's remuda, also froze to death. Not a cowboy in that outfit was over twenty years old.

The winter hailstorms brought only one good thing: dead jack rabbits. The men could find many of these animals lying about after the storm, and often they had them for dinner. As for the cowboys themselves, the hailstones caused many a knot on the head and cuts on the backs of hands.

Indians and horse thieves also plagued the cowboys on the trail. Whenever a herd was passing through Indian territory, the Indians would ride up and demand a toll—usually in the form of beef. The cowboys sometimes kept a few strays in the herd for just such occasions, and they would cut out one or more of these animals when stopped by Indians. The Indians often proceeded to kill and carve up the animal on the spot.

If the cowboys did not pay the demanded beef, or "Wohaw," as the Indians called it, the Indians were likely to cause the herd to stampede.

Horse thieves dogged the trails and stole from the remudas whenever they found the opportunity. Later, the problem became so widespread that some stock growers' associations took on the job of trying to rid the plains of these thieves. When caught, the horse thieves were often hung or shot on the spot.

Another hazard to be faced was the lack of water. Between the Pecos and the Canadian River, for example, there wasn't a drop of water for ninety miles. Even if the herd was pushed hard, it took a full day to cover only fifteen miles.

During the long, dry stretches, the cattle had to be

watched every moment, and they had to be handled with extreme care. It was hot and dry; there was no wind; and the dust hovered over the herd and the men. In such situations the cowboys would keep the cattle moving way into the night before allowing them to bed down; the cattle would be tired, and the cool night would take the edge off their thirst. Next morning, at daybreak, they would be put on the trail again.

Andy Adams' *The Log of a Cowboy*, a famous book on the cowboy, contains a description of a dry cattle drive over the Western Trail. On the third night without water, all hands were required to hold the herd. The cattle would not even lie down, but stood about restlessly. The next day was another of intense heat, and after only two hours on the trail, the "heat became unbearable to man and beast."

Here is Adams' account of what happened: "The lead cattle turned back several times, wandering aimlessly in any direction, and it was with considerable difficulty that the herd could be held on the trail. The rear overtook the lead, and the cattle gradually lost all semblance of a trail herd. Our horses were fresh, however, and after about two hours' work, we once more got the herd strung out in trailing fashion; but before a mile had been covered, the leaders again turned, and the cattle congregated into a mass of unmanageable animals, milling and lowing in their fever and thirst.

"The milling only intensified their sufferings from the heat, and the outfit split and quartered them again and again, in the hope that this unfortunate outbreak might be checked. No sooner was the milling stopped than they would surge hither and yon, sometimes half a mile, as ungovernable as the waves of an ocean. After wasting several hours in this manner, they finally turned back over the trail, and the utmost efforts of every man in the outfit failed to check them. We threw our ropes in their faces, and when this failed, we resorted to shooting; but in defiance of the fusillade and the smoke, they walked sullenly through the line of horsemen across their front. Six-shooters were discharged so close to the leaders' faces as to singe their hair, yet, under a noonday sun, they disregarded this and every other device to turn them, and passed wholly out of our control.

"In a number of instances wild steers deliberately walked against our horses, and then for the first time a fact dawned on us that chilled the marrow in our bones—*the herd was going blind.*"

Unable to manage the herd, and not knowing what lay ahead, the cowboys decided to turn back and head for the last watering place. The herd itself had already started back, and it could not be stopped. The cowboys overtook the herd, which was moving along at a "three-mile gait," and strung out nearly five miles. Eventually they reached water, the cattle "wading out into the lakes until their sides were half covered, and they would stand and low in a soft moaning voice, often for half an hour before attempting to drink."

Later, the herd was moved out on the trail again, but this time over a new route, veering off westward. The drive continued without another comparable dry stretch on that trip.

Going into unfamiliar country, it was the job of the trail boss to scout ahead for water. At times this meant putting himself a full day's distance ahead of his herd. When the cattle were brought up for watering, they would be spread out along the river bank, with the lead cattle placed downstream. As the rest of the cattle came to the water, they would go in upstream from the lead. In this way the entire herd would get clear water to drink.

Too much water could also be a problem. Heavy rains swelled the rivers. The Colorado, Brazos, Red, Washita, North Canadian, and Arkansas rivers all lay between San Antonio and Abilene. In bad weather these could be very treacherous. When these rivers were full and running fast, men, cattle, and horses died during the crossings.

During one drive the cowboys found the north fork

Sudden storms and floods might start a stampede that ended in the loss of many head of cattle

of the Canadian River very high because of heavy rains. They succeeded in getting the cattle into the water only to have them start to mill in midstream. By the time the mill was broken up and the herd safely across, 116 cattle and three horses had drowned.

Another time, while crossing the Red River with 4,500 head of cattle, the cowboys managed to put 1,000 over the first day; however, because of high winds and waves, they could not get any more over. Confident that it would not be too long before the river dropped, three men were put across with enough food for supper that night and breakfast the following morning. Their job was to keep the 1,000 head from straying. The weather continued bad and the water high, and the men on the far bank went without food for forty-eight hours.

Despite all the hardships, the cattle drives continued from 1866 until 1896, the year the last herd went up the trail.

In 1866, the number of cattle taken up the trail was 260,000. That year, however, proved to be a disaster. There was no established market for the cattle. The men were certain they could sell their cattle, although no one knew to whom or to where the animals might be delivered. For the most part they just hoped for the best. The route they followed led through extremely rough country, and the men were largely inexperienced in long-distance trail work and unprepared for the hardships on the way. Indians stopped the drives at every opportunity, levying taxes or stampeding the cattle—then demanding money for rounding them up again. At the Kansas and Missouri borders the cowboys were met by hostile ranchers who had not forgotten the effect Texas fever had had upon their cattle in pre-Civil War days. As a result, many cowmen abandoned their herds or sold them at great losses; others turned the herds westward to find a new route. Some made it; many did not.

The hard lessons of 1866 carried over to the following year, and few men were prepared to brave the trail. In 1867, only 35,000 cattle went up from Texas. But 1867 was also the date of the establishment of Abilene, Kansas, as a cattle depot. This was one of the most significant events in the development of the cattle trade.

Joseph G. McCoy was a young man of thirty when he approached officials of the Union Pacific Railway with the idea of establishing a rail head at Abilene. Until that time, the end of the rail line was at Salina, Kansas. McCoy knew the importance of getting cattle to a point served by rail, for with this accomplished, immense markets to the east would be opened up. Abilene was a good location, and cattle could make the drive to this point without touching the eastern part of Kansas.

In 1868, the cattle flowing out of Texas worked up

to 75,000. In 1869, the dam broke, and 350,000 cattle made the trip, most of them to Abilene. By 1871, this figure rose to a staggering 600,000.

Great numbers of these cattle moved up the Chisholm Trail. This was the most famous of the cattle trails and was named for a half-breed Indian trader—Jesse Chisholm. Not a cattleman, Chisholm did not move cattle up the trail that bore his name; he used it to take supplies into the Indian territory. As the trail drivers worked their way north they came upon "Chisholm's trail" and they followed it for its 225-mile length. Later, the entire trail from San Antonio, Texas, to Abilene, Kansas, became known as the Chisholm Trail.

There were other trails—the Western Trail ran from Bandera, Texas, to Ogallala, Nebraska; the Shawnee Trail began at San Antonio, Texas, and went to Baxter Springs, just over the Kansas line. A spur of this trail was the West Shawnee Trail, which had as its terminal point Junction City, Kansas.

Although the year 1871 appeared to mark historic heights for the cattle industry, ultimately it was a gigantic fiasco. Of the 600,000 cattle trailed north, only half were sold immediately and shipped east. The remaining 300,000 were held over on the Kansas plains during the winter of 1871-2. The reason for this was that many of these cattle had been judged unfit for marketing, either because of age or physical condition, and a layover until spring gave the animals the opportunity to take on fat. Another problem was that the need for stock cattle for the central and northern plains was not great enough to absorb all the cattle brought north that year.

The winter was one of the worst ever seen in that region. Losses reached 250,000 head. As a result, only 350,000 cattle went up the trail in 1872. The following year, however, confidence had been re-established and the count climbed to 405,000.

But trouble struck again. In 1874 the winter was rough, and prices dropped as a result of the financial depression of 1873. The cattle moved up the trail during 1874 numbered only 166,000. This figure slipped to approximately 151,000 the following year. Then the pendulum swung again. New ranges were opened in Colorado, Wyoming, Montana, and Dakota. Kansas and Nebraska lost their positions as the great cattle markets. In 1876, the cattle moved north amounted to nearly 322,000. The great boom was on.

6 · Trail's End

✻

THE SKYROCKETING BOOM of the cattle industry also meant the beginning of the end for the cowboy, although this end was still two decades away.

The railroads had begun to push westward and southward with increasing speed and number. The Northern Pacific reached Bismark, in Dakota, by 1873, and the Missouri, Kansas and Pacific stretched its finger deep into Texas.

Over the bright steel rails came the settlers, investors, and castaways from the East; the unemployed, gamblers, gunmen, and adventurers, all of whom looked to the Promised Land of the West as a haven, a land of adventure, or a place to make a fortune.

These men came by the thousands. Over a twenty-year span, they jumped the population of Kansas from 100,000 to 1,000,000. Nebraska had but 28,000 inhabitants in 1862, but by 1882 the count stood at 500,000.

Dakota, Colorado, Wyoming, and Montana gained more slowly, but the presence of the "nester"—the homesteader—came to be felt there as well.

Abilene, located 200 miles west of Kansas City and once the end of the trail for hundreds of thousands of Texas cattle, had already breathed its last as a cattle depot by 1871. The advancing railroads moved civilization steadily westward. Dodge City, the most famous of all the cow towns, took the mantle of leadership from Abilene, only to pass it on to Ogallala, Nebraska.

As the settlers moved west they took up land near available water, erected fences around their "spreads," and prepared to farm the land. The "free grass" of the range began to rapidly disappear, and the cowboys coming up from the trails found fences where before there had been none. They had only two choices—cut the fences and move the herds through, or swing the herds to the west, around the fences.

Sometimes when the nesters and the cowboys clashed there was "war," for each saw the other as the enemy and the one at fault. One of the earliest and most vicious of these range wars was the now famous Lincoln County War of 1878.

This "war" was concerned not only with range

rights but with personal jealousies, a fact that makes it less typical of this type of conflict. On one side of the fight was John Chisum, a cattleman with enormous holdings in New Mexico along the Pecos River. He hired his cowboys without question, and amassed a bunch of the toughest men on the range.

The Chisum brand was a straight bar running from shoulder to tail on the left side of his cattle. In addition, Chisum's animals were earmarked with a "jingle bob"—a mark so distinctive that his herd became known as the Jingle Bob, and his cowboys "Jingle Bob" riders. The ears were sliced so deeply that the bottom half flopped alongside the cow's face, making the animal a sorry looking sight.

The herds were huge and the landholdings great. Along the Pecos valley Chisum was king, except in the eyes of the settlers and smaller cowmen, who were jealous of his power.

The settlers' leader was L. G. Murphy, an ex-army-officer. Murphy had a store and a hotel, handled cattle contracts, lent money, and served as a "fence" for rustled cattle and horses. He had two partners, James Dolan and John Riley, and they held sway over a considerable piece of territory.

Chisum decided to back financially a mercantile and banking business in Lincoln to drive Murphy out of business. The business was run by John Tunstall,

Skirmishes erupted between the nesters and the cowboys

an Englishman, and Alexander McSween, a lawyer—
an arrangement that allowed Chisum to remain in the
background. Murphy was furious over this threat to
his territory. He was also angered because McSween
had refused to defend some of his men who were up
on charges of rustling cattle from Chisum. He re-
solved to take action through a sheriff "friendly" to
his side.

A short time later, the sheriff's posse headed out to
the Tunstall ranch to seize some horses and cattle as
part of a trumped-up legal claim. Leading the posse
was Billy Morton. They took Tunstall, and on the return trip to Lincoln he was killed. The murder
brought the fight out into the open.

Tunstall's foreman, Dick Brewer, had himself appointed a deputy by a justice of the peace, and he
gathered a posse several weeks later to track down
the killers. Billy the Kid rode out with them.

Brewer and his men overtook Billy Morton and
Frank Baker, both charged with Tunstall's murder,
and cornered them in a dugout. The killers held out
until they ran out of ammunition and then surrend-
ered under a promise of safe conduct. The two men
never made it back to Lincoln alive. Also dead was a
member of Brewer's posse who had argued against
killing the two men and was shot for his trouble.

The war was now on in full. Armed riders were

everywhere, and one could not always tell whether they were friendly or hostile until it was too late. People stayed off the streets and rarely ventured outside of their homes.

The toll mounted. Sheriff Brady and his deputy, George Hindman, were gunned down near the courthouse in Lincoln by Billy the Kid and four other men. The next to go was "Buckshot" Roberts, a former soldier and Texas Ranger. "Buckshot" had the distinction of driving off fourteen attackers, despite the fact that he was badly wounded. The attacking party included the Kid and Brewer, but by the time the gang quit the fight, Brewer was dead. The rest fled without getting their man that day. However, "Buckshot" died of his wounds on the following day.

On July 14, 1878, a wild battle was fought in Lincoln. It was the showdown fight, and both sides were prepared. The McSween-Tunstall bunch took up positions in McSween's house, with some of them spreading out to other vantage points. The battle went on for three days. When it was over, McSween and three of his men were dead. One was dead on the other side. Billy the Kid escaped.

In October 1878, General Lew Wallace was appointed governor. He issued a pardon to all men who had been involved in the "war" if they would agree to keep the peace. Though "action" flared up one more time, in the form of a murder, the Lincoln County War was over.

Meanwhile, the cattle drives kept rolling on, despite these and other early signs of impending trouble. Over 200,000 had trailed north in 1877; 265,000 the year Lincoln County became famous; 258,000 in 1879; and nearly 400,000 in 1880.

A quarter of a million head went out of Texas each of the next three years, although the squeeze was getting stronger. Kansas showed particular resentment at having Texas cattle within its borders. In his book *My Life on the Range*, John Clay noted that by the summer of 1882 a few grangers had already settled on land north of Dodge City, and that their feelings broke into "open revolt" the following year. He relates that his outfit was stopped by men who demanded cash to allow the cattle to pass. The Texans did not want to pay, but the shotguns aimed at them changed their minds. In that year, however, another 250,000 head went north.

The following season saw the drovers putting 420,000 cattle on the northern plains—the largest number brought up the trail since 1871.

The cattlemen were riding the crest of a gigantic boom. Prices were high and everyone was talking profit and how to make even more. Books were being circulated which told of the uncountable wealth possible to even modest investors in the cattle business.

New lands continued to open up as the Indians were pushed farther and farther west and north. Most of the Comanches and Kiowa were on reservations, and their lands were marked for settlement. The end of the Indians' independence had been hastened by the wholesale slaughter of the buffalo—the Indians' chief source of food and clothing. With the buffalo gone, the Indian found it necessary to depend on the white man's help.

In 1885, a quarantine act was passed in Kansas forbidding the entry of Texas cattle except during the months of December and January, because of the Texas fever problem. By restricting the drives to the dead of winter, the quarantine act dealt the death blow to an already poor Kansas market. The drives to the northern plains, however, showed no sign of flagging.

Everyone still wanted to get into the cattle business. Big investment companies were formed in the East during the early 1880s for the purpose of cattle speculation. Men arrived from Scotland, Germany, England, and other lands in great number. Books and word-of-mouth rumors had promised riches, and these men came to claim the reward.

The cattle were everywhere, and despite what the books had said, the grass was not inexhaustible. In fact, the summer of 1885 found the range dry and the grass short. Many of the trail herds were in poor condition. That same year, President Cleveland sent troops to force the cattlemen to clear their cattle off the Cheyenne-Arapaho reservation in Indian territory. As a result, an additional 200,000 cattle were put on the already overcrowded ranges outside of the reservation.

The winter was a hard one, particularly in the Texas Panhandle. Because of the weakened condition of the cattle, losses were heavy. However, apparently no one saw the danger signs. No one quite understood that the cycle was likely to repeat itself. The drive north during the summer and fall of 1886 was heavy. The northern ranges were jammed. The grass was scarce, and the cattle were weak. The stage was set for disaster.

The snow began in November. In January, a "chinook"—a period of sudden warming—set in. The snows began to melt, uncovering the badly needed grass for the cattle.

This blessing was short lived. Several weeks later the chinook ended, the snow began, and the diving temperatures and howling winds buried the grass under snow and ice. Unlike horses, cattle do not eat snow, and do not know how to paw the snow away to expose the grass beneath. Cattle began to starve and freeze to death by the thousands.

The big blizzard was one of the worst ever seen on

Blizzards were a hazard and many cattle perished from cold and starvation during prolonged snowstorms

the plains. Temperatures sank beyond thirty degrees below zero. The snow was many feet deep. When the winter ended, the cattlemen began to count up their losses. In some cases, the loss was 90 to virtually 100 per cent of the Texas cattle, while 30 to 60 per cent of the native cattle died. One man, who could count 5,500 cattle at the start of winter, recorded only 100 survivors later.

The blow was fatal to the cattle industry. Entire companies folded up. Many men were broken financially and spiritually. Great numbers of investors from Europe and the eastern United States gave up and returned home.

After 1887 the number of cattle on the trail steadily declined. Meanwhile, the bad feelings between the cattlemen and the ranchers began to erupt again. Added to this was a big jump in cattle rustling, and very often—to the cattlemen, at least—the nester and rustler seemed the same.

The cattlemen banded together to form "associations" in order to bring better organization to range affairs. They also decided to pool their resources and men in a great effort to rid the plains of cattle rustlers and horse thieves. One of the most notable associations was the Wyoming Live Stock Growers. Their members owned more than two million cattle, and their power and influence was strong. Both nester and rustler soon felt its sting.

The first sign of trouble appeared in 1889. Ten riders rode up to a store owned by James Averill. They took Averill and a friend, Ella Watson, known as "Cattle Kate" and hanged them both. A court trial was later held, but no one was convicted of the crime.

Then, on June 4, 1891, three men approached the ranch of a man named Tom Waggoner, showed false papers, and marched him off under arrest. When Waggoner was found on June 12, he was dead.

The settlers were not intimidated by the murders. The newspapers rose to the defense of the settlers, and everyone talked of how to defend their rights against the big cattle ranchers. On November 1, the cattlemen struck again; this time they bungled an attempt to murder two men, Ross Gilbertson and Nathan Champion.

Orley Jones, a twenty-three-year-old rancher, was next in line. He was ambushed and killed on November 28. On November 30, J. A. Tisdale, returning from Buffalo, Wyoming, to his ranch some sixty miles away, was also ambushed.

The cattlemen then met secretly to plan the "invasion" of Johnson County. They intended to make an example for all to see, and they carried with them a "dead list" of seventy men slated for death, including the county sheriff, Red Angus.

The cattlemen set out to recruit their men, and according to A. S. Mercer in his *The Banditti of the*

Plains, offered wages of five dollars a day plus a bonus of fifty dollars if a rustler was killed.

Twenty-five men were collected at Cheyenne. This band took the train to Casper, joined with a group of twenty-six men hired from Texas, and pushed off on horseback for Buffalo.

The original plan was to ride to Buffalo, kill Angus and his men, and take control of the town. Then, operating from this home base, the riders would sweep the surrounding country free of "rustlers."

On the way to Buffalo, word reached them that two of the men they wanted—Nick Ray and Nate Champion—were at the KC Ranch on the north fork of the Powder River. The riders quickly changed their plans and headed for the KC.

The men surrounded the cabin, taking care not to be seen. Two trappers who emerged from the house were captured, and a short while later Nick Ray stepped through the front door. Ray was hit at once by bullets, but was dragged back into the safety of the cabin by Champion, who dashed out under fire to rescue his friend.

The siege continued throughout the day, with Champion singlehandedly holding off the entire raiding party. Ray, meanwhile, had died from his wounds.

In the afternoon, Jack Flagg, also wanted by the men, came near the ranch on his way to Douglas.

With him was his seventeen-year old stepson. Flagg was on horseback, riding about 150 yards behind the boy, who was driving a wagon. Reporting the incident, Flagg said: "When the wagon hove in sight, the murderers jumped up and commanded the boy to halt, but he urged up his horses and drove for the bridge. When they saw he would not stop, one of them took aim on the corner of the fence and fired at him. The shot missed him and scared his team, which stampeded across the bridge and on up the road.

"There were twenty men behind the stable, and seven came up on horseback, three from one side of the road and four from the other and closed in behind me. When the men behind the stable saw me, they began to jump for their guns, which were leaning against the fence, and called on me to stop and throw up my hands. I did not comply with their order, but kept straight for the bridge. When I got to the nearest point to them—forty-seven steps—a man . . . stepped from the crowd and, taking deliberate aim at me with his Winchester, fired. Then they all commenced firing. I threw myself on the side of my horse and made a run for it. The seven horsemen followed me. When I overtook my wagon, which had my rifle on it, I told my boy to hand it to me, which he did; I then told him to stop and cut one of the horses loose and mount him. The seven horsemen were following me, and when I stopped, were 350 yards behind, but as soon as they saw I had a rifle, they stopped. I only had three cartridges for my rifle, and did not want to fire one of them, unless they came closer, which they did not seem inclined to do."

The raiders knew that they were going to be in for trouble, for surely Flagg would spread the alarm. They quickly loaded a wagon with hay and wood, pushed it against the beseiged cabin and set it afire.

Throughout the battle, Champion had managed to find time to jot down his thoughts on paper. An amazing story of a man under fire, it read, in part: "Me and Nick was getting breakfast when the attack took place. . . . Nick is shot, but not dead yet . . . they are shooting and are all around the house . . . bullets coming in like hail. . . . I don't think they intend to let me get away this time . . . there was a man in a buckboard and one on horseback just passed. They fired on them as they went by. I don't know if they killed them or not. . . . I guess they are going to fire the house tonight . . . shooting again. . . . It's not night yet. The house is all fired. Goodbye, boys, if I never see you again. Nathan D. Champion."

When the flames became unbearable, Champion made a dash for safety, but two hundred yards away from the house he fell at last. When he was found later, a note was pinned to his shirt which said: "Cattle thieves beware."

The riders then set off at a fast run in an effort to reach Buffalo before sunrise. Some twelve miles out from the town, they were met by a man who warned them of danger ahead. The townspeople had organized a large number of men who were on the way for a showdown fight.

The raiders headed at once for the TA Ranch on Crazy Woman Creek to prepare a defense. The next morning found the men completely surrounded by the huge local force. The battle continued for two days, with no losses on either side. The local men then conceived the idea of rolling a "go-devil" against the ranch house. The "go-devil" was made up of the running gear of two wagons fixed side by side with a framework of heavy logs. This was to be moved slowly forward, and it was thick enough to protect men crouched behind it. The plan was to move it close enough to the walls to allow the men to toss dynamite.

The movable fort was within 100 yards of the TA ranch house when troops from Fort McKinney arrived to halt the fighting. The raiders were returned under guard to Fort Russell, near Cheyenne. The Johnson County War was over, a sad defeat for the organized cattlemen.

The defeat was one more reminder that an era had

ended. It was too late to fight the settlers, railroads, sheepmen, or anyone else. The march of civilization could not be stopped. The great cattle drives were over. In 1896, the last herd made the drive, and the trails closed forever.

7 · *Cowboys Past and Present*

※

THE OLD-TIME COWBOY is gone, along with the long-horn and the fenceless range.

Was there something romantic in what the cowboy did? The answer is yes if there was romance in being caught on the plains in a rainstorm and having to sleep in soaked clothing and under soggy blankets. The answer is yes if there was romance in shaking drifting snow from blankets every morning and, in the thick of a blizzard, riding out to turn drifting cattle.

Perhaps this was romantic to the people who did not have to live it. But to the cowboy riding far out on the range with a storm sweeping out of the north, it was a time of trial.

In the summer the sun burned the grass, dried the streams, and wilted men's spirits. However, the cow-boy, as one anonymous writer of that day said, went on with his work "and did the best that was in him—for a few dollars for a month of his time, services, and for his knowing how."

These were the men who passed away with the vanishing trails. "Quiet, rather self-contained men, perfectly frank and simple," Theodore Roosevelt said. They were pioneers who paved the way for civilization.

The cowboy still exists today, but the old ways are gone except in some areas of south Texas, the Panhandle, and parts of the Dakotas. And on the San Carlos Reservation in Arizona, Apache punchers still round up, brand, and then drive their big Hereford herds along the trail to the nearest rail point, seventy-five miles and five days away.

But for the most part the trail drive is out of date. Fences, railroads, farms, and roads have seen to that. The era of mechanization has changed the life of and the need for the cowboy. The modern cowboy still gets up early, and his hours are often long and hard. He still rounds up the herd and brands the calves. Today, however, the cowboy rides out to the range in a jeep or a pickup truck, hauling his horse behind in a trailer. To check on cattle on the range in winter, helicopters and light planes are sometimes used for spotting. Some ranchers have found another useful vehicle in a ski-mounted machine driven by an airplane propeller. This winterized version of the "swamp buggy" gives them a previously unobtainable mobility over their snow-covered ranges.

The trail drive has been replaced by the cattle truck, which delivers the cattle right to the railroad, and the trains cover in a day or so ground that took many months of hard trail work eighty-five years ago. And the old longhorn? This rugged slab-sided animal has long been replaced by such breeds as the Brahman, Hereford, Angus, Shorthorn, Charolais, and Charbray.

While there are instances today where the cowboy's job is virtually unchanged from what it used to be, he is more commonly a ranch hand, a jack-of-all-trades. Where he was once simply a horseman hired to do "cow work," he now drives a truck and a tractor as well. Often he is college educated, having attended a school such as Texas A. & M. or the university of Arizona or Wyoming. He has a strong interest in agriculture, and is concerned not only with cows but with animal husbandry, irrigation planning, and plant and animal hybridization.

Most ranches today are also farms, and to be profitable they must be run efficiently and make use of the most modern tools and techniques available. Cattle raising and ranching are complex and vast operations that are still growing. As the population and wealth of the country continues to rise, so does the demand for beef. Per-capita beef and veal consumption in 1975 is estimated at 110 pounds, an increase of 35 per cent over 1964. To meet this projected demand, more than 11 million additional cattle will have to be killed annually. The extent of the cattle business today can be realized by a look at the current cattle population: 107 million as of January 1966.

And what of the cowboy today? How does he live, and what does he look like? Many ranches have caught up with the times. They have electric lights, television, and radio. They have deep-freezes to keep the food fresh, and trucks bring hot meals to the cowboys too far out from the home ranch to "come and get it." Social Security and hospitalization plans cover most of the ranch hands, and retirement is carefully planned for.

Today's cowboy is better paid than the old-timer, has more free time and more things to do with it. He no longer needs to be the rugged individual leading a solitary life. Now he often brings his wife with him, and many ranches provide special quarters to accommodate the pair. He is older—the average age is about thirty—than the cowboy of a century ago.

The cowboy is as distinctive in his dress today as he used to be. He is instantly recognizable not only in the small ranch and cattle towns, but also on the streets of Phoenix, Tuscon, Dallas, Alberquerque, and El Paso.

Though the cowboy rides less now, he still wears

Today trucks deliver cattle to the railroad where they are loaded on stock cars

boots, favoring the high-topped style just as the old-timer did. His hat is usually a Stetson, with a brim three to three and a half inches wide. Vests, however, have nearly vanished, and gloves are worn only during the winter months. Chaps and the old yellow slicker are as universally popular as ever. His pants are Levis, his work shirt is denim. He sports a denim jacket most of the time, and wears his hat with a flat crown. And if the rider of today wants it—though not all do—he can buy a saddle for his horse complete with quilted or sponge-rubber seat.

There is little doubt that the call of the cowboy life is muted now. It is a pale shadow of its former self. Yet the cowboy still rides where and when he can, still brands and works with cows, though he may now heat his branding iron in a portable rig fired by butane. The old-time cowboy had a strong streak of individuality in him, took to the outdoors like a duck to water, and would not have wanted any other job. He loved his work and took great pride in it. These things apply to the modern cowboy as well.

As Theodore Roosevelt put it back in 1888, hard as the cowboy's existence is, "it has yet a wild attraction that strongly draws to it his bold, free spirit."

8 · Lingo

THE COWBOY had a language all his own. It sounded like gibberish to the tenderfoot, but it suited the cowboy's needs, and in this respect was not much different from the vocabulary used by men today who are employed in highly specialized professions.

The words and phrases which follow represent only a bare outline of the terms used by the cowboy.

Aboard   On horseback
Adios   Goodbye
Adobe   Clay; used to make houses
Airtights   Canned goods
Anti-godlin   In a roundabout way
Arroyo   Small stream or dried river bed
Band   A number of horses together
Bear sign   Doughnut
Beef   Cattle four years old or more

Bit   Part of the bridle that goes into the horse's mouth, and to which the headstall and reins are attached

Blend trap   Corral used to catch mustangs; trap is camouflaged so as not to be seen

Bog rider   Cowboy who looked for cattle caught in bogs

Bonnet string   Hat strap or thong

Box canyon   Gorge or ravine with one closed end

Brakemen   Men who were not good at riding or handling cattle; hired because of a shortage of experienced cowboys

Brand artist   Rustler

Brasada   Brush country; a part of lower Texas covered with thickets and underbrush

Broomtail   Range mare

Cactus boomers   Longhorn cattle from the Texas brasada

Can openers   Spurs

Chaps   Heavy leather pants legs worn over regular pants to protect a rider in rough brush country

Cinch   Strap to bind the saddle to the horse

Coasters   Longhorn cattle from the Texas Gulf Coast

Concha   Flat metal disk, usually of silver, for decoration on hats, chaps, spurs, etc.

Cow hunt   A roundup in the early trail days

Cow sense   Smartness; a compliment when attributed to a cowboy; when used to describe a horse it meant the horse was a particularly good horse

Cut   A group of cattle separated from the main roundup herd

Cutter   Six-shooter

Cutting a rusty   Courting; also, doing your best

Dally After roping, to take a turn around the saddle horn with the rope to keep it from slipping

Die-up Wholesale death of cattle, usually during a severe winter

Drag riders Cowboys who rode behind a trail herd to keep the slow and weak cattle moving

Drift Cattle moving with a storm

Droop-eyes Calves who had had their eyelid muscles cut so that they could not see to find their mothers

Dry stock Cows not giving milk

Eye-baller Nosy person

Fagging Moving fast

Fairground To rope an animal by the head, throw the rope over its back while its still running, and then throw the animal to the ground

Fence rider A cowboy who rode along fence boundaries checking for breaks, rustlers, etc.

Fence stretcher Tool for stretching fence wire from post to post

Flankers Men who rode alongside the trail herds to keep them in line

Fork a horse To mount a horse

Fox fire Phosphorescence; seen on horses' and cows' ears during electrical storms

Fuzzies Ranch horses

Galluses Braces; suspenders

Goosey man Nervous man

Grappling irons Spurs

Gun outfit A group of cowboys having a reputation for wildness and toughness

Gyp water   Water, usually fed by underground springs, that has a strong quinine and salt taste

Hackamore   Halter; to which the reins are attached

Hair in the butter   A delicate situation

Heifer   One-year-old cow

Henskins   Thin blankets

Hobbles   Cuffs joined by lengths of rope or leather; used on two of a horse's legs at night to keep him from straying far

Hog-tie   To hold an animal down by tying three of its legs together

Hoodlum wagon   Wagon containing supplies of wood and water for camp

Jayhawkers   Lawless gangs in Kansas; name sometimes given to settlers who took up claims where the Texas herds watered, and charged the cowboys a fee to use the water

Lariat   From the Spanish *la reata*; a rope

Leggins   Chaps

Lick   Syrup

Lobo   A wolf

Long horse   A horse capable of long-distance travel at good speed

Maverick   Unbranded animal with no known owner

Mill   A herd going in a circle

Mixed herd   A herd made up of male and female cattle

Moon hunter   A horse that keeps his head up when running

Mossy horn   Longhorn cattle six or more years old

Mount of horses   Usually nine in number

Muleys   Cows without horns

Mule skinner   A teamster or freighter who drove a freight wagon on a regular route

Nester   Small farmer

Nighthawk   A horse wrangler on night guard

Outlaw   A horse that cannot be broken

Peeler   A good bronco or wild-horse rider

Pilgrims   Imported cattle

Point riders   Men who rode up near the front of a trail herd

Possum belly   Sling fixed under a chuck wagon to hold fuel

Pup hole   Deep hole made by a prairie dog

Putting the string on her   Roping a cow

Quirt   A whip; one end was usually tipped with lead

Rawhides   Derisive name for Texas cowboys

Reading sign   Following a trail

Remuda   The extra horses held at the roundup ground or driven with a cattle herd for the cowboys' use

Rep   A cowboy who represented his home ranch during the roundups on the open range, cutting out and driving home cattle belonging to his boss

Riding the grubline   Visiting from one cow outfit to another; usually when the cowboy was out of work during the winter

Road brand   Special brand put on all the cattle in a herd going up the trail if they were not all from one ranch

Roustabout   Jack-of-all-trades around a camp

Rustler   Cattle thief

Sagebrush men Northern cowboys

Scabbard Open-topped, but otherwise enclosed, sheath for a rifle

Scatter gun Shotgun

Sea lions Longhorn cattle from the Gulf Coast of Texas

She stock Female cattle

Shinnery Scrub oak; brush

Side line To tie two of an animal's feet, on the same side

Slicker Yellow raincoat

Slinging the catgut well Expert roping

Son-of-a-gun A favorite cowboy stew

Soogan A heavy quilt

Stake rope Used to picket a horse

States' eggs Eggs imported from the East

Stayed out with the dry cattle Made a night of it in town

Straw boss Assistant to the trail boss

Stray men Men working on a roundup who do not belong to the cattle outfit owning the roundup wagon

Swing riders Men who, like the flankers, rode alongside the trail herd

Tally man Man who recorded the brand and sex of calves being branded

Tie-fast man Cowboy who tied his rope to the saddle horn, rather than taking a turn, or dally, around it

Tonsil varnish Whisky

Trail drivers Cowboys who took cattle up the trail

Waddy Another name for cowboy; sometimes used to describe a cowboy-turned-rustler

War bonnet   Hat

War sack   Bedroll containing a cowboy's belongings

Wet stock   Cattle smuggled from Mexico

White house   The boss's house

Wide place in the road   Small town

Windy   A farfetched story

Wipes   Neckerchiefs

Wohaw   Indian name for beef

Work   Refers to roundups and branding

Wrangler   Man who takes care of the remuda

Bibliography

✹

ABBOTT, E. C., and HUNTINGTON, HELEN. *We Pointed Them North.* New York: Farrar and Rinehart, 1939.

ADAMS, ANDY. *The Log of a Cowboy.* Boston: Houghton Mifflin, 1903.

ADAMS, RAMON F. (ed.). *The Best of the American Cowboy.* Norman, Oklahoma: University of Oklahoma Press, 1957.

——*Cowboys Lingo.* Boston: Houghton Mifflin, 1936.

—— *The Old-Time Cowhand.* New York: Macmillan, 1961.

—— "The Range Cook's Steaks and Stews." Phoenix, Arizona: *Arizona Highways*, Vol. 30, No. 7, July 1954.

—— *Western Words. A Dictionary of the Range, Cow Camp and Trail.* Norman, Oklahoma: University of Oklahoma Press, 1944.

BENEDICT, C. P. *A Tenderfoot Kid on Gypwater.* Dallas, Texas: Texas Folklore Society; The University Press, 1943.

BLACK, A. P. "The End of the Long Horn Trail." Selfridge, N.D.: *The Selfridge Journal*, n.d.

BLACKER, I. R. (ed.). *The Old West in Fact*. New York: Obolensky, 1962.

BRANCH, DOUGLAS. *The Cowboy and His Interpreters*. New York: D. Appleton, 1926.

BRISBIN, J. S. *The Beef Bonanza; or, How to Get Rich on the Plains*. Norman, Oklahoma: University of Oklahoma Press, 1959. First published in 1882.

CLAY, JOHN. *My Life on the Range*. Privately printed, 1924. Reprinted by Antiquarian Press, New York, 1961.

COOK, J. H. *Fifty Years on the Old Frontier*. Norman, Oklahoma: University of Oklahoma Press, 1957. First published in 1923 by Yale University Press.

COOLIDGE, D. *Arizona Cowboys*. New York: E. P. Dutton, 1938.

DALE, E. E. *Frontier Ways*. Dallas, Texas: University of Texas Press, 1959.

——— *The Range Cattle Industry*. Norman, Oklahoma: University of Oklahoma Press, 1960.

DOBIE, J. FRANK. *The Longhorns*. Boston: Little, Brown, 1941.

——— *A Vaquero of the Brush Country*. Dallas, Texas: The Southwest Press, 1929.

DRIGGS, H. R. *Westward America*. New York: Somerset Books, 1942.

FLETCHER, R. H. *Free Grass to Fences*. New York: University Publishers, 1960.

FOSTER–HARRIS. *The Look of the Old West*. New York: Viking Press, 1955.

FRANTZ, J. B., and CHOATE, J. E. *The American Cowboy: The Myth and the Reality*. Norman, Oklahoma: University of Oklahoma Press, 1955.

GIPSON, F. B. *Cowhand: The Story of a Working Cowboy*. New York: Harper, 1953.

GRANT, BRUCE. *The Cowboy Encyclopedia*. Chicago: Rand McNally, 1951.

HOUGH, EMERSON. *North of 36*. New York: D. Appleton, 1923.

——— *The Story of the Cowboy*. New York: D. Appleton, 1897.

HOWARD, R. W. *This Is the West*. New York: Rand McNally, 1957.

HUNTER, J. M. (ed.). *The Trail Drivers of Texas* (two vols). San Antonio, Texas: The Old Trail Drivers' Historical Association; Jackson Printing Co., 1920, 1923.

JAMES, WILL. *The American Cowboy*. New York: Scribner's, 1942.

——— *Cowboys North and South*. New York: Scribner's, 1924.

KING, DAN. "Up the Chisholm Trail." *True West Magazine*, Vol. 8, No. 5. May–June 1961.

McCOY, JOSEPH G. *Historic Sketches of the Cattle Trade of the West and Southwest*. Kansas City, Missouri: Ramsey, Millett & Hudson, 1874.

McMILLAN, E. L. "The Cowboy, Product of His Environment," *West Texas Historical Association Yearbook*, Vol. 31, October 1955.

MERCER, A. S. *The Banditti of the Plains*. Norman, Oklahoma: University of Oklahoma Press, 1959. First published in 1874.

MORA, JO. *Trail Dust and Saddle Leather*. New York: Scribner's, 1946.

POST, C. C. *Ten Years a Cowboy*. Chicago: Rhodes and McClure, 1904.

RAINE, W. M., and BARNES, W. C. *Cattle, Cowboys and Rangers*. New York: Grosset & Dunlap, 1930. Published originally as *Cattle* (Doubleday, Doran & Co. 1930).

RISTER, C. C. "Social Activities of the Southwestern Cowboy." *West Texas Historical Association Yearbook*, Vol. 7, June 1931.

ROLLINS, P. A. *The Cowboy*. New York: Schibner's, revised and enlarged edition, 1936.

ROOSEVELT, THEODORE. *Ranch Life and the Hunting Trail*. New York: Century, 1896.

SIRINGO, C. A. *A Texas Cowboy; or, Fifteen Years on the Hurricane Deck of a Spanish Pony*. Chicago: M. Umbdenstock and Co., 1885.

TINKLE, L., and MAXWELL, A. (eds.). *The Cowboy Reader*. New York: Longmans, Green, 1959.

WARD, F. E. *The Cowboy at Work*. New York: Hastings House, 1958.

WESTERMEIER, C. P. "The Cowboy—Sinner or Saint." *New Mexico Historical Review*, Vol. 25, No. 2, April 1950.

WILSON, R. R. *Out of the West*. New York: Wilson-Erickson, 1936.

Index

Index